MW00596452

CONTENTS

Author: **William Alexander**
Editor-in-Chief: Richard W. Wheeler, M.A.Ed.
Editor: Jean M. Turner
Richard Morse
Consulting Editor: Howard Stitt, Th.M., Ed.D.
Revision Editor: Alan Christopherson, M.S.

Alpha Omega Publications®

804 N. 2nd Ave. E., Rock Rapids, IA 51246-1759
© MCMXCVII by Alpha Omega Publications, Inc.   All rights reserved.
LIFEPAC is a registered trademark of Alpha Omega Publications, Inc.

TWO WORLD WARS

Conditions in Europe became increasingly unsettled in the early 1900s as nations grew more suspicious of one another. Attempts at peaceful negotiations failed. European nations grew further apart, producing a climate that led to war following the assassination of the Archduke Ferdinand of Austria-Hungary. World War I was a time of unprecedented devastation and suffering.

This LIFEPAC® deals with the tensions that led to World War I. It examines the strategies and tactics of the Allied nations and the Central powers in the Great War and the Allied drive that brought the Central powers to surrender.

After studying the terms of the Peace of Paris, you will explore postwar attitudes in the 1920s and 30s, the military rearming of Germany and Italy, and their aggressive policies that led to the Second World War. You will study World War II, the Allied victory, and the formation of the United Nations. Finally, you will study the growth of communism and its struggle with the free world.

OBJECTIVES

Read these objectives. They tell you what you will be able to do when you have successfully completed this LIFEPAC.

When you have finished this LIFEPAC, you should be able to:

1. Identify the causes of the mounting tension among European nations in the late 1800s and early 1900s.

2. Describe the developments that caused European nations to form the Triple Alliance and the Triple Entente.

3. Outline the hostilities on the European front in World War I.

4. Explain the negotiations, the terms, and the effects of the Peace of Paris.

5. Describe the attitudes that prevailed among nations following World War I.

6. List the factors leading to World War II.

7. Outline the major battle strategies of the Allied and Axis powers in World War II.

8. List the terms of the peace settlements for both Germany and Japan after World War II.

9. Describe the organizations and efforts of nations to preserve peace after World War II.

Survey the LIFEPAC. Ask yourself some questions about this study. Write your questions here.

_____

_____

_____

_____

_____

_____

_____

_____

_____

_____

I. WORLD WAR I

In the late nineteenth and early twentieth centuries, conditions in Europe became increasingly tense as national leaders grew more impatient and more uncertain of each other. Tensions arose that eventually led to war.

SECTION OBJECTIVES

Review these objectives to learn what you should be able to do when you have completed this section.

1. Identify the causes of the mounting tensions among European nations in the late 1800s and the early 1900s.

2. Describe the developments that caused European nations to form the Triple Alliance and the Triple Entente.

3. Outline the hostilities on the European front in World War I:
    3.1   List the strategies and victories of the Germans in the first years of the conflict.
    3.2   Describe the Allied drive across France and Belgium resulting in German surrender.

VOCABULARY

Study these words to enhance your learning success in this section.

armament	imperialism
conscription	nationalism

Note: All vocabulary words in this LIFEPAC appear in **boldface** print the first time they are used. If you are unsure of the meaning when you are reading, study the definitions given.

MOUNTING TENSIONS

During the late nineteenth century, there was a rising spirit of **nationalism**, a sense of unity and loyalty of a people toward their country. Although national pride can work in a positive way, when carried to extremes, it leaves no room for compromise. Jealousies and suspicions between nations remain unresolved.

Nationalism. As nationalism grew in Europe, an earlier concept of self-sufficiency was revived. Nations sought through territorial expansion and colonization to fulfill material needs and to eliminate their dependency on rival nations for goods. This movement was known as **imperialism**. European nations began to look beyond their own borders for lands rich in raw materials for industry. These lands were either absorbed as colonies by political or military pressures, or were forced to trade their raw materials.

In such a setting, frictions between nations naturally arose, especially when several countries attempted to colonize in the same area. Africa, in particular, became a source of conflict between imperialistic European powers. In the Far East, a bitter war ensued between Japan and Russia as they clashed over Manchuria, a region in northeastern China.

Nationalism and imperialism were accompanied by the rise of powerful military establishments. Nations backed by strong armies and navies had an international advantage over weaker ones.

The German state of Prussia led Europe in military might. Its principles were adopted by nations throughout the world. Through **conscription** it drafted young men into military service. Prussian soldiers served a period of active duty after which they were assigned to a military reserve where they were subject to recall at any time. Prussia also distributed supplies and equipment throughout the country for use on short notice.

In addition to the military draft, Prussia introduced the concept of the general staff. Composed of highly trained and skilled officers, its task was to improve military equipment and training. It often conducted mock battles to test strategies and war plans.

As tensions increased in Europe, an armaments race began. National boundaries were fortified and guarded as nations increased their military preparedness.

A build-up also occurred at sea. Europe's traditional great naval powers, England and France, were challenged by Germany for superiority.

The **armaments** race strained the budgets of every nation involved. Taxes rose, but most citizens regarded the expense as part of their patriotic duty.

The race for military superiority created a dangerous situation on an unstable continent. Europe was headed for war.

Match these items.

1.1	_____ nationalism	a.	led Europe in military readiness
1.2	_____ imperialism	b.	improved military organization
1.3	_____ Prussia	c.	loyalty of people for their country
1.4	_____ conscription	d.	cause of war between Russia and Japan
1.5	_____ general staff	e.	build-up of war equipment
1.6	_____ Manchuria	f.	hostilities between Germany and Prussia
1.7	_____ armaments race	g.	colonization for gain
		h.	military draft

Complete this activity.

1.8   List the advantages and disadvantages of the following:

	Advantages	Disadvantages
a. nationalism	a.	a.
b. imperialism	b.	b.
c. military build-up	c.	c.

3

Alliances. In the late 1800s the separate German states merged to form the German Empire. While building its military strength, Germany maintained peace with its neighbors, with the exception of its long-time rival, France. Friction between Germany and France had been growing for years over the rich territory of Alsace–Lorraine, then under German control.

Under the leadership of Otto Von Bismarck, known as the *Iron Chancellor*, Germany sought to strengthen its position against France. Bismarck hoped to isolate France from its neighbors. He thus joined in the Dual Alliance between Germany and Austria-Hungary. It guaranteed that if one nation was attacked, the other would come to its aid. By forming the Dual Alliance, Bismarck increased Germany's strength. When Italy joined the Alliance in 1882, he had achieved his first goal of isolating France from its neighbors.

Bismarck then focused his attention on securing friendly political relations with Russia and England, nations likely to come to France's aid in time of war. England was intensely involved in colonial expansion, and Bismarck was careful not to challenge it.

Fear of a possible two-front war with France on the west and Russia on the east led Bismarck to maintain cordial relations also with Russia.

Bismarck was successful in his foreign policy against France until Kaiser Wilhelm II came to the German throne in 1888. He claimed his divine right to rule and to make foreign policy decisions himself. He interfered with Bismarck's policies to the extent that Bismarck finally resigned.

Wilhelm proceeded to destroy all that Bismarck had worked to achieve. Abrasively and with little sensitivity in foreign relations, Wilhelm proceeded to drive other nations to act in exactly the manner Bismarck had feared.

France had long sought allies to balance the power in Europe that had been upset by the formation of the Triple Alliance. When Russia needed a loan and requested aid from Germany, the Kaiser refused. France readily agreed to loan Russia the money, and this loan led to friendly relations between the two nations that resulted in an alliance in 1894. Bismarck's fear was then realized—Germany was flanked on either side by hostile nations.

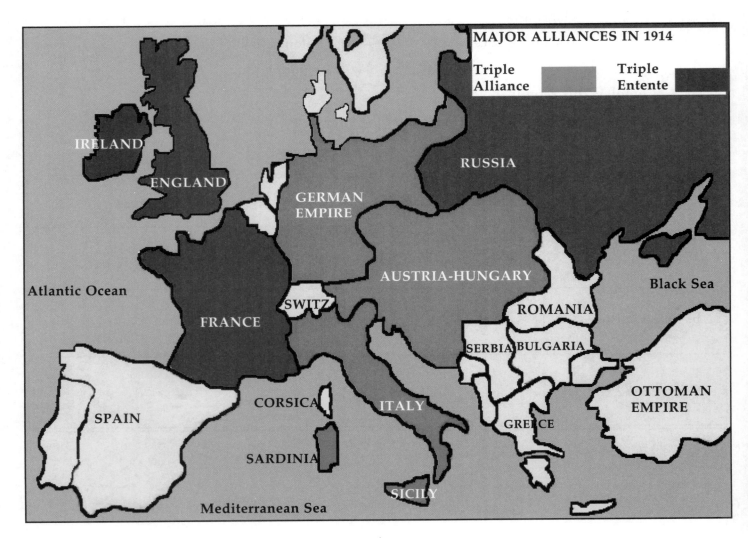

Wilhelm actively entered the competition for colonies with England, which Bismarck had carefully avoided. Challenging England's naval superiority, he boasted of his plan to develop the German navy into the best in the world. England tried to come to an agreement with Germany to limit the naval build-up on both sides, but the ambitious Wilhelm rejected the offer. England then sought allies against Germany. After working out their differences, England and France formed an entente. Then, with the assistance of the French, Russia and England settled their rivalries in the Near East, and the Triple Entente, or Allied Powers, was complete.

The formation of the Triple Entente restored the balance of power in Europe. The Alliance was centrally located and joined by common boundaries. The Entente, however, controlled the seas.

Both sides had internal differences, and disputes had to be resolved for them to remain allies. Nevertheless, the sides were chosen, and nations prepared for a conflict they had wanted to avoid.

Under Wilhelm, Germany continued to seek power beyond its borders. It began negotiations with Turkey to gain control over the Balkans to the south. It proposed the construction of a railroad from the German capital of Berlin through the Balkan states to Constantinople. Wilhelm's objective was to extend the railroad through the Near East to the Persian Gulf.

Russia and England were alarmed over Wilhelm's proposal. Construction of a railroad to Constantinople would interfere with English trade with the Near East and India. The alliance between Turkey and Germany, furthermore, would destroy Russia's hope of gaining control of Constantinople. The German plan accelerated mounting tensions among European nations.

ERUPTING CONFLICTS

Germany was not alone in its interest in the Balkan states. Turkey, Austria, and Russia all openly pursued interests in the area. Although Britain opposed any attempt by another country to control the Balkans and Constantinople, it nevertheless supported Russia in its opposition to Germany's bid for the disputed territory.

Fierce fighting erupted between the Balkan states of Serbia and Austria in the early 1900s. Serbia lost and was forced to give up valuable holdings to Austria.

Germany's interference in the Balkans further intensified these explosive conditions. Germany supported Austria's claim to the disputed area. Opposing Germany and Austria, however, were

Russia and England. Germany and France continued to contest the sensitive Alsace-Lorraine and colonies in North Africa. Italy wanted to free Italians who were living in Austrian-controlled territories, but seemed uncertain whether to remain in the Triple Alliance. In the midst of this instability, relations between Austria and Serbia came to a head.

Aggression. Serbian hatred of Austria resulted in the formation of many secret anti-Austrian societies in Serbia. On June 28, 1914, a member of a Serbian secret party shot and killed Archduke Francis Ferdinand, heir to the Austrian throne. Infuriated by the action, Austria determined to punish the Serbs.

Austria issued the Serbian government an ultimatum and insisted on an answer within twenty-four hours. Austria demanded, among other things, the right to suppress the anti-Austrian movement in Serbia and punish offenders as it saw fit. When Serbia only partially agreed to the Austrian demands, Austria declared war on the Balkan state.

The Austrian declaration of war set off a chain reaction among European nations according to their previously arranged alliances and agreements. With

Photo courtesy of R. Breen

World War I and World War II soldiers.

assurance of French support in case of war, Russia began to mobilize its troops near the Austrian border in defense of Serbia. When the German demand that Russia cease mobilization was ignored, Germany declared war on Russia. Within days fighting began. When France, a Russian ally, refused to remain neutral, Germany also declared war on France.

To avoid a long war on two fronts, Germany determined to defeat France quickly and attack Russia before the Russians were totally prepared to fight. Arousing the fury of the world, Germany marched across Belgium en route to France, in direct violation of Belgian neutrality. Germany's action brought about England's decision to join forces with France and Russia and to declare war on Germany. England immediately prepared to send troops to Belgium's defense.

Nearly a year later, Italy, realizing the only gains it could receive would be by Austrian rule, switched sides and joined forces with the Allies. This action was a shock to her former Alliance partners.

Japan, in accordance with its treaty of 1902, joined the war on the side of Great Britain. Turkey was later linked with the Central European powers. Few countries in Europe were able to avoid involvement; only Switzerland, Spain, Holland and the Scandinavian countries maintained their neutrality.

Germany's drive through Belgium to attack France succeeded. Although not altogether surprised at the German violation of Belgium's neutrality, France was alarmed at the size and effectiveness of the offensive. Invading troops approached the capital of Paris before a desperate French effort by soldiers, driven to the front line in taxi cabs from Paris, could halt the surprised Germans. A French counterattack followed along the entire front and the Germans were forced to retreat. The offensive not only saved the French capital but thwarted German hopes for a quick victory as well.

Russian resistance to the well-trained and disciplined Germans was not as effective. Poor equipment, over-extended supply lines, and weak leadership resulted in a steady retreat as the Germans broke through the center of the Russian front. Allied efforts to aid the battered Russians also met with defeat, giving Germany new confidence in its military capability.

With the hope of a quick German victory on the Western front shattered, the war had settled into a stalemate by 1916. On land it was fought largely in trenches with few gains and immense loss of life as generals hurled huge offensives at the enemy in attempts to overwhelm the enemy. At sea the situation was similar; the British navy blockaded Germany's North Sea supply routes while German U-boats attempted to cut off British shipping and trade to the island. As a result, neither side broke through to gain an advantage.

Because of the stand-off, both sides were eager to secure American support. Propaganda flooded the United States to convince Americans to rally to their cause.

Write *true* **or** *false*.

1.09 _____ Germany and France both wanted to control Alsace-Lorraine.

1.10 _____ Russia and Austria disputed the future of the Balkan states.

1.11 _____ The assassination of Ferdinand brought German-Serbian hostilities to a head.

1.12 _____ Germany hoped to defeat France before the Russians fully prepared for battle.

1.13 _____ While Russian resistance to Germany was effective, French resistance was weak and disorganized.

1.14 _____ The stalemate of 1916 resulted in trench warfare.

Answer the following question.

1.15 What should the Christian's stand be concerning military involvement?

_____

_____

_____

Teacher check _____

Initial   Date

6

List the alliance of each nation and their reasons for entering the war.

1.16

Nation	Alliance	Reasons for Entrance
a. Austria-Hungary	1.	2.
b. Germany	1.	2.
c. Russia	1.	2.
d. England	1.	2.
e. Japan	1.	2.
f. France	1.	2.
g. Italy	1.	2.

Counter-aggression. Americans had claimed neutrality from the beginning of European hostilities. The American people supported President Wilson when he said, "The war is one with which we have nothing to do, whose causes cannot touch us." Wilson maintained that the United States would remain free in order to "do what is honest…and truly serviceable for the peace of the world." America's non-involvement in the European conflict became increasingly difficult, however. Public opinion in the United States had been gradually favoring support of the Allied cause since 1914. The Germans unified this support of the Allies when their submarines attacked United States vessels off Allied coasts. Fear of war supplies being transported to England and France prompted this German naval policy even though it was in direct violation of international law. Germany reasoned that it had no alternative. Without a blockade of supplies to the Allies, Germany would lose the war.

The United States defied German warnings by continuing to ship supplies to the Allies. When a German U-boat torpedoed the British passenger ship the *Lusitania,* and killed over one thousand passengers including 124 Americans, German-American relations were severely tested. President Wilson rebuked the action. The Germans apologized and assured the United States that the incident would not be repeated. Germany resumed its attacks on neutral ships, however, causing more American deaths. The American people were ready to fight back.

German U-Boats

President Wilson prepared a message to Congress that resulted in an American declaration of war on Germany on April 6, 1917.

The entrance of the United States into the war raised the morale of the weary Allies. Germany tried to end the war before the Allies could be reinforced by fresh American troops. It launched a massive offensive on the western front made possible by the cessation of fighting in the East.

In March, 1917, an upheaval in Russia known as the Bolshevik Revolution overthrew the czar—and replaced the monarchy with a republican form of government. When the new government announced its intention to continue the war with Germany, however, the Russian people, weary of the conflict, revolted again.

The victors were members of the Bolshevik Party that became the Communist Party in 1918. The Communist Party was more interested in the establishment of

Western Front 1914-1918

Eastern Front 1914-1918

communism than in fighting an unwanted war. As a result, the Bolshevik leaders sought an armistice to end hostilities with Germany and withdrew from the conflict.

Having signed a secret peace pact with Russia, Germany could now combine troops from both the eastern and western fronts in a massive offensive against the French and British before they could be reinforced by the arrival of Americans.

Within days the German offensive recaptured all the territory taken by the Allies in two years. Attacking again, the Germans pushed the French back to Chateau-Thierry, forty-four miles from

Paris. The Allied cause looked bleak, but the exhausted French and British refused to give up.

The arrival of three American divisions helped stop the Germans. At Chateau-Thierry, Cantigny, and Belleau Wood, the Allied lines held. When the Germans began another offensive in July, the Allied forces, having been steadily reinforced with American troops, were ready with a counterattack of their own. The Germans fell back in retreat along the Somme through the Argonne Forest. Inspired by this Allied effort, even tiny Belgium attacked the Germans.

Following the Allied counterattack of 1918, German strength and morale dropped. Furthermore, their allies were collapsing all around. Bulgaria and Turkey, seeing no hope for victory, surrendered to the Allied powers. Austria-Hungary, dealt devastating blows by the Italians, also declared an armistice ending their involvement in the war.

Standing alone, Germany's armies retreated on all fronts. Faced with an invasion of their homeland, the German government also requested an armistice. After several days of negotiations, terms were agreed upon. On November 11, 1918, an armistice was declared. Six hours later World War I was over.

Much of Europe lay in ruins. The war had introduced new and more deadly weapons. Fortifications once thought invincible were shattered by gigantic cannons and aerial bombing, first from balloons and later by airplanes. Tanks and poison gas were also used.

World War I proved to be the most destructive conflict in history. In terms of money, the cost was figured at $350 billion; in lives lost it was even more staggering. An estimated ten million civilians were killed; military deaths totaled 8.5 million, and an additional 21.2 million were wounded in action.

The long war was over. A withdrawal of German forces began immediately, closely observed by Allied troops. The task ahead was also immense—the writing of a lasting peace.

Weapons of World War I

➤ **Complete the statements.**

1.17   The sinking of the *Lusitania* by Germany, along with other similar incidents, brought the
_____ into World War I.

1.18   Germany's hope to defeat the Allies in France before American troops arrived was aided by the
withdrawal of _____ from the war.

1.19   The Allied powers successfully halted the massive German drive at
_____ .

1.20   The party that governed Russia after the Russian Revolution, later renamed the Communist Party, was the _____ .

Write the letter of the correct answer on each line.

1.21   Allied victories which broke the German offensive of 1918 in France included all of the
        following locations *except* _____ .
        a. Chateau-Thierry
        b. Cantigny
        c. Berlin
        d. Belleau Wood
        e. Argonne Forest

1.22   The German defeat included all of the following factors except _____ .
        a. the collapse of their allies
        b. a strong Allied offensive
        c. the threat of invasion to the German homeland
        d. the withdrawal of Russia

1.23   New war equipment used in World War I included all the following items *except*
        _____ .
        a. tanks
        b. airplanes
        c. mines
        d. balloon bombing
        e. poison gas

 Complete this activity.

1.24   With a classmate, chart the following battles of World War I.

	Location	Strategy	Victor
a. 1914 German offensive across Belgium through France	a.	a.	a.
b. 1918 German offensive	b.	b.	b.
c. Chateau–Thierry	c.	c.	c.
d. Allied drive of 1918	d.	d.	d.

 Review the material in this section in preparation for the Self Test. The Self Test will check
        your mastery of this particular section. The items missed on this Self Test will indicate
        specific areas where restudy is needed for mastery.

SELF TEST 1

Match these items (each answer, 2 points).

1.01	_____ Wilson	a.	seized control of Russian government
1.02	_____ Bismarck	b.	organized Prussian military
1.03	_____ Wilhelm	c.	led Europe in military readiness
1.04	_____ Ferdinand	d.	fought over by Japan and Russia
1.05	_____ Bolsheviks	e.	settled differences with France
1.06	_____ Prussia	f.	fought over by Russia and Austria
1.07	_____ Manchuria	g.	the United States president during World War I
1.08	_____ Alsace-Lorraine	h.	an aggressive German kaiser, World War I
1.09	_____ Balkan states	i.	the Iron Chancellor of Germany
1.010	_____ general staff	j.	a territory mutually desired by France and Germany
		k.	the assassinated Austrian Archduke

Write the correct answer on each line (each answer, 3 points).

1.011   Loyalty of a people to their country is called _____.

1.012   Colonization by a larger nation to increase its economic standing is known as _____.

1.013   Bismarck strengthened his position against France by forming the _____.

1.014   The revolution in Russia that led to the takeover of the government and Russia's withdrawal from the war was known as the _____.

1.015   With the help of American soldiers, the Allied stand that halted the German advance in France was at _____.

1.016   Germany and Austria-Hungary were the major _____ powers of World War I.

1.017   The practice of drafting men into the military is called _____.

1.018   Tensions increased across Europe as the armaments-race resulted in huge _____ build-ups.

1.019   An incident that led the United States into the war was the sinking of the _____.

1.020   Two weapons that were first used in World War I were a. _____ and b. _____.

Write *true* **or** *false* (each answer, 1 point).

1.021   _____ Bismarck established peaceful relations with England and Russia to isolate France.

1.022   _____ The Triple Alliance was formed to rebalance power in Europe upset by Bismarck's Triple Entente.

1.023   _____ Wilhelm's abusive actions destroyed Germany's relations with England and Russia.

1.024 _____ Control of the Balkan states was fought for by Russia and Japan.

1.025 _____ The assassination of Archduke Ferdinand set off a chain reaction of nations declaring war.

1.026 _____ Germany's march through Belgium brought England into the war.

1.027 _____ While French resistance to the German advance was strong, Russia's was weak and disorganized.

1.028 _____ The stalemate of 1916 was characterized by trench warfare and naval blockades.

1.029 _____ Germany attempted to defeat the Allies before the Russians withdrew from the war.

1.030 _____ Russian withdrawal from the war allowed the strength of the German offensive in France to increase.

Write the letter for the correct answer on each line (each answer, 2 points).

1.031 The single event which led to World War I was _____.
  a. imperialism
  b. nationalism
  c. armaments race
  d. Ferdinand's assassination

1.032 A German action which increased tension in Europe was _____.
  a. its isolation of France
  b. the race for colonies
  c. the proposed railroad
  d. the naval build-up

1.033 A nation that did not side with the Allies in World War I was _____.
  a. Italy
  b. Japan
  c. United States
  d. Belgium
  e. Turkey

1.034 An event which favored the German position in 1917-1918 was _____.
  a. its stand at Chateau-Thierry
  b. the Russian withdrawal
  c. the victory at Cantigny
  d. an Allied drive through Argonne Forest

1.035 The German defeat was hastened by the _____.
  a. Russian Revolution
  b. armaments build-up
  c. collapse of German allies
  d. massive invasion of Germany

Answer these questions (each answer, 5 points).

1.036 What brought the formation of the following alliances?

  a. Triple Alliance _____

  b. Triple Entente _____

12

1.037　　　What was the significance of these events?

    a.　Assassination of Archduke Ferdinand _____

_____

    b.　German march across Belgium _____

_____

    c.　German U-boat attacks _____

_____

    d.　Russian Revolution _____

_____

    e.　Chateau-Thierry _____

_____

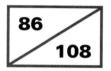

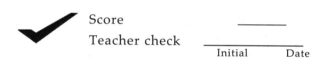

Score _____

Teacher check _____

Initial　　　Date

II. PEACE RETURNS

After four years of war, the world wanted a lasting peace. Woodrow Wilson's idealistic statement that World War I was "a war to end all wars" expressed the hope of people everywhere.

In this section of the LIFEPAC, you will study the Peace of Paris that followed the war. European nations wanted a harsh treaty for the Germans, whereas Wilson endeavored to soften its terms.

You will explore the conditions in war-torn nations. With the exception of the United States, World War I left its combatants economically exhausted.

You will also learn how the world fell into an economic depression and what factors led to recovery and eventual stability.

Finally, you will study the events that led the United States into a second world war.

SECTION OBJECTIVES

Review these objectives to learn what you should be able to do when you have completed this section.

    4.　Explain the negotiations, terms, and effects of the Peace of Paris:
       4.1 Explain the conflict between the advocates of a just peace and a harsh peace.
       4.2 List the terms of the Treaty of Versailles.

    5.　Describe the attitudes that prevailed among nations following World War I.

    6.　List the factors leading to World War II:
       6.1 Identify the economic factors leading to World War II.
       6.2 Outline the military aggression leading to World War II.

VOCABULARY

Study these words to enhance your learning success in this section.

demilitarize   fascism   totalitarian

recession   reparations

PEACE INITIATIVES

Determined to make the peace following World War I a lasting one, President Woodrow Wilson prepared a framework for that peace before the war was even over. He publicized his famous Fourteen Points for settlement early in hopes that the Germans would surrender more quickly.

Wilson reasoned that his Fourteen Points for peace would inspire Allied soldiers with goals for which to fight and would persuade Germany to surrender sooner with hopes of a fair and lenient peace. Copies of Wilson's proposals were dropped behind enemy lines.

Wilson's Fourteen Points included:
1. Open covenants of peace openly arrived at.
2. Freedom of the seas.
3. Removal of trade barriers between nations.
4. Reduction of armaments.
5. Impartial adjustments of colonial gains.
6. Evacuation of German troops from Russia.
7. Evacuation of German troops from and restoration of Belgium.
8. Restoration of France and the return to it of Alsace-Lorraine.
9. Readjustment of the Italian frontier.
10. Independent development for the peoples of Austria-Hungary.
11. Redrawing of the Balkan boundaries.
12. Self-determination for Turkey.
13. Independence for Poland and an outlet to the sea.
14. Formation of a general association of nations.

When the Germans signed the armistice on November 11, 1918, they hoped to receive a peace settlement based on the proposals outlined in Wilson's Fourteen Points. The German government received no guarantee it would, however. As losers, the Central powers were in no position to bargain.

The "Big Four" at Versailles Treaty Meeting. (Left to Right) Orlando, George, Clemenceau, Wilson

14

Settlements. A year after the Fourteen Points were publicized, the Allied nations came together in Paris to discuss the fate of the defeated powers. Over thirty Allied countries were represented at the meetings begun on January 18, 1919. The five great powers of England, France, Italy, the United States, and to a lesser degree, Japan, made the major decisions. The remaining nations were to participate later in the public writing of the peace treaty. Russia, which withdrew early from the war, was not represented.

As the Paris meetings got underway, Wilson's proposals were severely tested. His belief in a peace with justice found none of the support he had anticipated. Although Prime Minister David Lloyd George of Great Britain, Premier Vittorio Orlando of Italy, and Premier Georges Clemenceau of France had all initially agreed to the Fourteen Points, they maintained that the Central powers should be punished for starting the war. They wanted to divide and disarm Germany and to force it to pay **reparations**. Wilson, on the other hand, believed that a harsh peace would lead to another war.

The European countries—France, Italy, and England—along with Japan had much to gain by a harsh peace treaty with Germany. They desired to gain control of valuable German territories and colonies.

Realizing that he was losing support for his mild peace proposals, Wilson focused his energies instead on formation of a world organization, the *League of Nations*. It was written into the terms of the settlement. It had the authority to manage international relations, to limit armaments, and to settle disagreements between nations in a peaceful manner.

When the Peace of Paris was finalized, Wilson signed the treaty, although he was satisfied only with the establishment of the League of Nations.

In May 1919, representatives of the German government met to approve their section of the treaty. They were shocked by the harshness of its terms and disturbed that Wilson's Fourteen Points had not been followed. However, they could do little other than voice their disapproval. With few minor changes, negotiations on the treaty were over. The Germans signed at the Palace of Versailles on the outskirts of Paris on June 18, 1919; thus, the treaty was named the Treaty of Versailles.

The terms were severe. Germany was required to return Alsace-Lorraine to France and to surrender territory to Poland, Belgium, and Denmark, thus reducing its holdings by 13 percent from what they had been in 1914. German colonies in Africa and the Pacific were divided among the victorious nations. Germany was to be occupied by foreign troops. The German army was limited to 100,000 men and its navy to six battleships. The other Central powers—Austria, Hungary, Bulgaria, and Turkey—were also dealt with severely by the terms of the Paris Peace Treaty.

The end of World War I left bitterness that in a few years would lead to the rearming of Germany and a second world war.

Match these items.

2.1	_____ Fourteen Points	a. a peace treaty between Allied and Central powers following World War I
2.2	_____ League of Nations	b. armistice following World War I
2.3	_____ Treaty of Versailles	c. Wilson's proposals for peace after World War I
2.4	_____ Peace of Paris	d. organization for world peace
		e. organization for world peace segment of the Peace of Paris dealing with Germany

Match these leaders with their country.

2.5 _____ Lloyd George   a. Italy

2.6 _____ Wilson   b. Russia

2.7 _____ Orlando   c. United States

2.8 _____ Clemenceau   d. France

                                                   e. Britain

Write the correct letter on each line.

2.9 The Allied power not represented at the Paris peace talks after World War I was _____ .
   a. Italy
   b. United States
   c. Russia
   d. England
   e. France

2.10 The Paris peace talks settled the _____ .
   a. reparations paid by Germany
   b. future of the Central powers
   c. armistice terms
   d. occupation of France

2.11 The Treaty of Versailles _____ .
   a. withdrew occupation troops from Germany
   b. gave Alsace-Lorraine to Belgium
   c. divided German colonies and territory
   d. limited French armament

Answer this question.

2.12 Work with a friend and list arguments for and against Wilson's just peace following World War I.

   a. for _____

   _____

   _____

   _____

   _____

   b. against _____

   _____

   _____

   _____

   _____

   _____

Attitudes. After the war, Americans reacted against further participation in international affairs. Fearing it might eventually lead them into another conflict, the United States Senate rejected the passage of Wilson's League of Nations. The Senate's decision shocked the president, who believed rejection of the league would result in a future war.

When the United States refused to join the League of Nations, other nations lost hope in the idea. Without United States membership, the League of Nations lacked the strength it needed to keep international peace. The American public was tired of war, however, and they were no longer interested in causes and reforms.

After a brief postwar **recession**, the American economy enjoyed one of the most prosperous periods in history. Due to mass production techniques, productivity rose. New automobiles, houses, and modern appliances were widely available. Jobs were plentiful, and wages increased. The 1920s were a prosperous time.

Other nations did not enjoy similar prosperity, however. Staggering war casualties left England, France, Belgium, and Russia drained of manpower. Industrial production declined. Prices and unemployment rose, leaving thousands of people in Europe destitute. Industrial areas had suffered severe damage and some nations were depending heavily on the payment of German reparations in order to rebuild. Germany was bitter, believing it had been tricked into surrender by the promises held out in Wilson's Fourteen Points. It was crippled by the harsh terms of the Treaty of Versailles. Its land had been divided, its possessions taken away, and its pride crushed when it was forced to take blame for the war. Reparations payments, set at 33 billion dollars, were especially burdensome to the exhausted German economy.

To collect their reparations, France and Belgium sent military forces into Germany. The action was the final blow to the German economy, which collapsed in 1923. Unemployment and hunger followed.

In an attempt to help Germany out of its economic crisis, the United States instituted the Young Plan. It reduced German reparations payments to this country so Germany could pay its other war debts. Americans invested in German industry to allow Germany to repay other European countries so they, in turn, could make payments to the United States for their debts.

Other European countries borrowed money from the United States to repay each other. That money was then sent back to repay America. In effect, then, the United States was lending money to pay itself.

Thus, when America plunged into the Great Depression of 1929, the entire world followed.

➡ **Write** *true* **or** *false*.

2.13 _____ America supported Wilson in his plan for lasting world peace.

2.14 _____ America enjoyed a prosperous economy during the 1920s.

2.15 _____ Although the British and French economies were prosperous following the war, they had suffered severe loss of manpower.

2.16 _____ France and Belgium needed German reparations to rebuild their countries.

2.17 _____ Germany placed much of the blame for its economic plight on the harsh terms of the Treaty of Versailles.

2.18 _____ The European nations were dependent on American loans, and when the American depression struck in 1929, it affected the whole world.

➤ **Answer these questions.**

2.19   a. Why did the United States reject the League of Nations? _____

_____

_____

   b. What effects did this rejection have on the League of Nations? _____

_____

_____

2.20   What comfort did the Bible offer to Christians in the economic depression of the 1920s and
1930s? Research this question with a classmate and write your findings here.

_____

_____

_____

_____

_____

POWER QUESTS

The depression of the 1930s did not strike the United States alone. Because of the dependence of European nations on American loans, it resulted in world-wide hunger and unemployment.

Economic. Germany's economy, in particular, was in desperate condition due to the heavy burden of war reparations. Under the weight of these payments, the German economy collapsed in 1923. Money was of so little value that a small purchase required a wheelbarrow full of currency. The German government responded by creating a new mark equal to one trillion of the old ones. This eliminated the large debts of the poor, but it was disastrous for the middle class. Savings were destroyed. In many cases businessmen suddenly owned less than laborers. Such a financial climate fostered the rise of an authoritarian government.

Communism in Russia after the Revolution of 1917 was **totalitarian**, exercising complete control over the people. Totalitarianism assumed two forms—communism in Russia and **fascism** in Italy. Both attempted to control all aspects of individual lives.

Fascism emerged in Italy under Benito Mussolini. Through violence he rid Italy of communists and established himself as dictator. He concentrated on

Hitler addressing the Reichstag after invading Poland, September, 1939.

18

building Italy's military might, and the growth of industry for military purposes brought Italy out of depression. Unemployment decreased as factories produced war supplies and soldiers left jobs open to join the army and navy.

Germany, too, became more authoritarian as economic hardships mounted. The German people resented the harsh treatment of the Treaty of Versailles, which they blamed for their economic woes. They wanted a firm hand to restore the economy. In desperation, the nation's financial leaders backed the appointment of Adolf Hitler as chancellor under President Paul von Hindenburg in 1933. As he promised, Hitler lowered unemployment; he did it, however, by building up the German military in direct violation of the Treaty of Versailles. Hitler also cut unemployment among the nation's youth by establishing the National Socialist (Nazi) Party youth movement.

Japan's ambitions had also increased by the late 1930s. An industrial country, it lacked natural resources. Thus, it sought to control territories rich in raw materials. In 1931 Japanese soldiers seized Manchuria. When Japan declared Manchuria independent of China, China protested to the League of Nations. The league rebuked Japan, which withdrew from the world organization and continued its expansion.

Continued Japanese aggression in China touched off a full-scale war between the two nations in 1937. The destruction in China was immense. The Japanese economy flourished, however, as war production increased.

Three nations in the 1930s—Germany, Italy, and Japan—had solved their economic dilemma by rearming. Along with the growth of their military might, however, came a desire for power.

Match these items.

2.21 _____ communism

2.22 _____ fascism

2.23 _____ totalitarianism

2.24 _____ Mussolini

2.25 _____ Hitler

2.26 _____ National Socialist Party

2.27 _____ Paul von Hindenburg

a. the Italian dictator

b. a government having complete control over its people and activities

c. Russian totalitarianism

d. Republican government

e. the president of Germany

f. Italian totalitarianism

g. the German chancellor

h. Hitler's Nazi organization

Write *true* **or** *false*.

2.28 _____ Germany's economy was near collapse due to the harsh terms of the Treaty of Versailles.

2.29 _____ The frustration of European depression gave rise to democratic governments.

2.30 _____ Communism and fascism are two forms of totalitarianism.

2.31 _____ Germany, Italy, and Japan increased their military might to recover from their economic depression.

2.32 _____ Japan's seizure of Manchuria led to increased Japanese expansion through China and the Pacific.

➡ **Answer this question.**

2.33   How does military growth affect a nation's economy? _____

_____

_____

_____

_____

_____

Military. As Italy's military power grew, Mussolini, the Italian dictator, decided to use it to build an Italian empire. He began his expansion in Ethiopia, an African nation that Italy failed to colonize in 1896 when an Ethiopian army defeated invading Italian troops.

In October, 1935, Italian soldiers once again marched into Ethiopia. Haile Selassie, the Ethiopian emperor, appealed to the League of Nations to halt the Italian invasion. The league could do nothing. Ethiopia fought courageously, but the Italians were more numerous and better armed. In the spring of 1936, Mussolini's troops occupied the capital of Ethiopia. Selassie fled; and Mussolini, the Italian dictator, gave himself the added title of "emperor."

Italian aggression in Ethiopia showed the weakness of the League of Nations. It had failed to protect a weak nation against aggression and was no longer taken seriously.

After President von Hindenburg died in 1934, Hitler combined the offices of president and chancellor. With the enthusiastic support of the German people, he became dictator. By 1935 Hitler was blatantly breaking many of the restrictions imposed on Germany by the Treaty of Versailles. In these actions he was unchallenged by other European nations. When Hitler marched his troops into the Rhineland, a section of Germany near the French and Belgian borders that had been **demilitarized** by the peace treaty, France did nothing to retaliate.

In 1938 Hitler determined to take control of Austria. When he threatened war, Austria gave in.

Hitler next put pressure upon Czechoslovakia. Three million Germans lived in a portion of that country awarded to Czechoslovakia after World War I. Hitler insisted they be allowed to govern themselves within the Czechoslovakian state; however, his ultimate goal was to make the former German territory a part of his Third Reich. When European powers met to settle the dispute, Hitler was given control of that part of Czechoslovakia inhabited by Germans.

The rest of Czechoslovakia came under German control in 1939. This further aggression caused British and French leaders to realize that appeasement was encouraging Hitler in his aggression. Europe's period of peace was coming to an end.

When Hitler tried to regain control of former German territory awarded to Poland at the end of World War I, he placed the British and French in another dilemma. The territory was inhabited mostly by Germans. Hitler insisted on bringing them into his Third Reich, as he had done with Austria and Czechoslovakia.

The world wondered whether France and England would come to the defense of Poland or allow Hitler to seize its territory. Before the question was answered, however, more shocking news came—Nazi Germany and Communist Russia had signed a treaty. Both nations, displeased with the terms of the 1919 Peace of Paris, had ignored it.

Nevertheless, the Poles resisted not only German demands but also British and French pleas to negotiate with Hitler over its threatened territory. Hitler prepared to attack. When the Poles further refused to meet his demands, the German invasion of Poland began on September 1, 1939.

The days of appeasement were over. Britain and France, in accordance with their earlier agreement to help Poland in case of attack, declared war on Germany two days later. They would be joined later by the Soviet Union and the United States, forming the Allied Powers. Germany and Italy would be joined by Japan, forming the Axis Powers. World War II had begun.

HISTORY & GEOGRAPHY

1008

LIFEPAC TEST

62 / 77

Name _____

Date _____

Score _____

HISTORY & GEOGRAPHY 1008: LIFEPAC TEST

Match these items (each answer, 2 points).

1. _____ Bismarck   a.   designed United Nations Charter

2. _____ Mussolini   b.   Russian premier, World War II

3. _____ Wilhelm   c.   built up German military in violation of Treaty of Versailles

4. _____ Wilson   d.   British prime minister, World War II

5. _____ Roosevelt   e.   head of American forces in the Pacific

6. _____ Hitler   f.   his assassination sparked World War I

7. _____ Churchill   g.   head of fascist Italy

8. _____ Eisenhower   h.   led French attack on Germans at Paris

9. _____ MacArthur   i.   set up Triple Alliance for German defense

10. _____ Ferdinand   j.   originator of Fourteen Points and League of Nations

11. _____ Rommel   k.   led Allied invasion of Normandy

12. _____ Stalin   l.   German ruler in World War I

                                                     m. commander of German forces in North Africa

Complete these statements (each answer, 3 points).

13. The section of the Peace of Paris dealing with Germany was the _____ .

14. Colonization of a smaller nation for a larger nation's profit is called

_____ .

15. Britain, France, and Russia formed the _____ to balance European power after the formation of the Triple Alliance.

16. The organization established after World War II for settlement of world problems without war was the _____ .

17. In World War I, Allied powers fought the Central powers; in World War II, the Allies fought the _____ powers.

18. Totalitarianism assumed two forms–in Italy it was fascism and in Russia it was

_____ .

19. Wilson's proposed organization for peace after World War I was the _____ .

20. Loyalty of a people for their country is called _____ .

21. The city blockaded by Russia in 1948 was _____ .

22. A government totally controlling its people is called a _____ government.

Write *true* **or** *false* (each answer, 1 point).

23. _____ Wilhelm supported Bismarck in maintaining positive relations with England and Russia.

24. _____ While French resistance in World War I against the Germans was strong, Russian resistance was weak and disorganized.

25. _____ German U-boat attacks forced the United States to declare war on Germany in World War I.

26. _____ Advocates of a lenient peace finally succeeded in drawing up the Treaty of Versailles.

27. _____ The German economy was crippled by the harsh terms of the treaty following World War I.

28. _____ Japan began its aggression by seizing Manchuria; Italy began by seizing Ethiopia.

29. _____ World War II peace treaties were constantly disrupted by German aggression.

30. _____ U.N. forces were involved in freeing the country of Kuwait during the Persian Gulf War.

31. _____ The branch of the United Nations which takes action is the Security Council.

32. _____ World War II peace settlements were constantly deadlocked between the United States and Russia.

Write the letter of the correct answer on the blank (each answer, 2 points).

33. The nation that did not side with the Allies in World War I was _____ .
    a. Italy
    b. Japan
    c. Belgium
    d. Turkey
    e. United States

34. The acquisition of additional territory by a country through unlawful or aggressive means is called _____ .
    a. republicanism
    b. imperialism
    c. nationalism

35. The government of Russia during World War I and World War II was _____ .
    a. democratic
    b. imperialistic
    c. communist
    d. fascist

36. Allied victories in World War II included all of the following battles except _____ .
    a. North Africa
    b. Normandy invasion
    c. Chateau-Thierry
    d. Guadalcanal
    e. Iwo Jima
    f. Berlin

2

Complete this item (this answer, 5 points).

37.   Describe as many of the factors as you can from this LIFEPAC which led to World War II.

_____

_____

_____

_____

_____

_____

_____

_____

_____

NOTES

Complete these statements.

2.34   Mussolini sought Italian expansion by invading Ethiopia, whose leader was _____
_____ .

2.35   Selassie sought aid against the Italians from the _____ .

2.36   To expand his nation's power, Hitler defied the terms of the _____
_____ .

2.37   The Peace of Paris was ignored when a treaty was made between Germany and
_____ .

2.38   The German act that led to the beginning of World War II was the invasion of
_____ .

Write the letter of the correct answer on the blank.

2.39   Aggressive nations seeking to expand their power in the 1930s did not include _____ .
    a. Japan   c. Germany
    b. France   d. Italy

2.40   The nation that was not invaded by Hitler's troops was _____ .
    a. Austria   c. Italy
    b. Czechoslovakia   d. Poland

2.41   The nation not taking an active involvement against the German invasion of Poland was
included _____ .
    a. England   c. Poland
    b. France   d. the United States

SelfTest Review the material in this section in preparation for the Self Test. This Self Test will check your mastery of this particular section as well as your knowledge of the previous section.

SELF TEST 2

Match these items (each answer, 2 points).

2.01	_____ Wilson		a.	head of Italian fascism
2.02	_____ Bismarck		b.	Russian emperor, World War I
2.03	_____ Wilhelm		c.	French leader, Peace of Paris
2.04	_____ Ferdinand		d.	German chancellor turned emperor
2.05	_____ Bolsheviks		e.	Ethiopian emperor
2.06	_____ Mussolini		f.	Czechoslovakian leader
2.07	_____ Hitler		g.	Italian leader; Peace of Paris
2.08	_____ Hindenburg		h.	German chancellor isolating France
2.09	_____ Selassie		i.	the assassinated Austrian archduke
2.010	_____ Orlando		j.	originator of the Fourteen Points and League of Nations
2.011	_____ Clemenceau		k.	German dictator, World War I
2.012	_____ George		l.	the head of British government, Peace of Paris
			m.	controlled Russian government after Russian Revolution
			n.	president of Germany

Complete these statements (each answer, 3 points).

2.013   The proud loyalty of a people for their country is called _____ .

2.014   The United States aided the postwar German economy with the _____ Plan.

2.015   A government controlling all aspects of its people's lives is called a _____ government.

2.016   The World War I peace treaty dealing with Germany was called the _____ .

2.017   A stronger nation's colonization of a weaker nation is _____ .

2.018   The peace meetings after World War I were held in _____ .

2.019   Wilson's proposals for world peace after World War I were called the _____ _____ .

2.020   Payments by defeated nations for damages suffered during war are called_____ .

2.021   Wilson's organization to maintain lasting world peace was called the _____ _____ .

2.022   Mussolini's form of totalitarianism was called _____ .

Write *true* **or** *false* (each answer, 1 point).

2.023   _____ The Triple Entente was formed by Bismarck to equalize the power in Europe that was upset by the formation of the Triple Alliance.

2.024   _____ Germany, Italy, and Russia formed the Triple Alliance.

2.025   _____ German actions such as the sinking of the Lusitania brought the United States into World War I.

2.026   _____ Germany, Austria-Hungary, and Turkey were three of the Central powers.

2.027 _____ Because other nations were dependent on American loans, America's Great Depression affected them all.

2.028 _____ The negotiations between Russia and Germany increased the fight against the terms of the Fourteen Points.

2.029 _____ France and Belgium invaded Germany to demand reparations.

2.030 _____ Japan began its territorial expansion by seizing Manchuria.

2.031 _____ Aggressive nations in pre-World War II years were Japan, Germany, and Italy.

2.032 _____ Mussolini sought military expansion by invading Ethiopia.

Write the letter of the correct answer on each line (each answer, 2 points).

2.033 All of the following items were factors leading to World War I *except* _____.
   a. death of President Paul von Hindenburg
   b. imperialism
   c. military build-up
   d. United States interference
   e. Ferdinand's assassination
   f. German aggression

2.034 Leading to the German defeat in World War I were all of the following steps *except* _____.
   a. Allied drive of 1918
   b. collapse of German allies
   c. American entrance into the war
   d. withdrawal of Russia from the war
   e. threat of invasion of German homeland

2.035 Harsh terms dealt to Germany by the Treaty of Versailles included all of the following actions *but* _____.
   a. Alsace-Lorraine given to France
   b. German territory given to Belgium and Denmark
   c. division of German colonies
   d. withdrawal of occupation troops from Germany
   e. reduced German military

2.036 The postwar period was marked by all of the following factors *except* _____.
   a. American prosperity
   b. lack of manpower and morale among European Allies
   c. increased American world involvement
   d. struggling German economy
   e. bitterness among Central powers

2.037 Factors leading to World War II included all of the following situations *except* _____.
   a. Great Depression
   b. rise of authoritarian governments
   c. aggression by Germany, Italy, Japan
   d. strength of League of Nations
   e. German invasion of Poland

Answer these questions (each answer, 5 points).

2.038   How did the Treaty of Versailles lead to World War II?

_____

_____

_____

_____

2.039   How did Hitler and Mussolini lift their nations out of economic crisis?

_____

_____

_____

Complete this activity (this answer, 5 points).

2.040   List the steps of Hitler's aggression leading to World War II.

_____

_____

_____

_____

_____

✓ Score   _____
Teacher check   _____
                 Initial   Date

III. WORLD WAR II

Hitler's thirst for power led him to try to regain the territory taken from Germany by the Treaty of Versailles following World War I. The invasion of Poland began a second world war, which was far more costly than the one that ended twenty years before.

In Section III of this LIFEPAC, you will study the events that led to the outbreak of World War II in Europe. You will learn about United States support of its European allies and this nation's decision to become involved in the conflict.

You will also explore the war with Japan and the campaigns in the Pacific theater.

Finally, you will learn about the war's end, the peace settlement, and the role of the United Nations in world affairs.

Review these objectives to learn what you should be able to do when you have completed this section.

7. Outline the major battle strategies of the Allied and Axis powers in World War II:
    7.1 Describe the battles on the Western front.
    7.2 Explain the American strategy on the Pacific front.

8. List the terms of the peace settlements for both Germany and Japan.

9. Describe the organizations and efforts of nations to preserve peace after World War II.
    9.1 Outline the organization and functions of the United Nations.
    9.2 Explain the attempts of free-world nations to counteract the growing power of communism.

VOCABULARY

Study these words to enhance your learning success in this section.

blitzkrieg	ratification
kamikaze	reprisal

BATTLE FRONTS

As in Czechoslovakia, Hitler's invasion of Poland was a success. Within two weeks, western Poland was under German control.

The German victory was largely the result of a new tactic. Known as **blitzkrieg** (lightning war), it combined dive bombers, tanks, modern guns, and a strategy of encirclement by ground soldiers, which surprised and confused the enemy.

The Soviets also marched into Poland, and the Poles were forced to sign an armistice with the Russians as well.

Western. Their military drive begun, Russia moved on to the Baltic states. Estonia, Latvia, and Lithuania were forced to permit Russian military installations within their borders. The Russians then insisted that Finland allow a Russian naval base in its country. The demand was rejected, and Russia attacked Finland. The Finns shattered Russian hopes for a quick victory with a courageous defense but were finally crushed by Russians in superior numbers. The Soviet position in the north was strengthened.

After these initial German and Russian victories, fighting on the western front stopped; in fact, newspapers began referring to it as a phony war. A blitzkrieg against Denmark and Norway in April, 1940, put an end to such talk.

Within weeks, German troops seized control of the two Scandinavian nations, giving them strategic positions on the North Sea. The irregular Scandinavian coastline was an ideal site for submarine bases, from which French and British shipping was now threatened.

Before the Allies were able to counterattack, the blitzkrieg struck again against Holland, Belgium, and Luxembourg. The strength and speed of the German attack forced the British army to retreat from the continent back to England. With the French forces weakened, Mussolini, who had been neutral, joined sides with Hitler. Italy's declaration of war on Britain and France was a shock to the beleaguered Allies.

Striking out across the Belgian plain, Hitler moved on France. France was not prepared for the German attack. The French had little alternative but to sign an armistice on June 22, 1940.

Great Britain was left to face Hitler alone. The Germans moved quickly. Bombing raids on English cities caused great destruction.

In September, 1940, Japan joined the Axis powers. The future for the Allies looked bleak.

After nearly a month of German bombing raids, Hitler offered the British government a chance to surrender. Prime Minister Winston Churchill said, "We shall never surrender"; and England braced for more attacks.

Germany stepped up its air raids on England. Tons of explosives were dropped on the island every day, but the British refused to give in. Responding to British appeals, the United States shipped arms and equipment. The United States, too, was now preparing for war. The *Selective Service Act* of September, 1940, began drafting young men to fight.

Hitler now turned his attention to the remaining Balkan states. Rumania and Bulgaria fell to German offensives. Unable to defend themselves, Yugoslavia and Greece surrendered.

Greece provided an excellent launching point for the German campaigns in North Africa where the Suez Canal was a major German objective. Led by General Erwin Rommel, known as the *Desert Fox*, Axis forces drove the British from Libya into Egypt. In the Middle East, however, the enemy was blocked by the British and free French who held their ground in Iran, Lebanon, and Syria.

Following the German takeovers in the Balkan states, cooperation between Germany and Russia began to crumble.

Ignoring the pact between them, Hitler launched a sudden invasion of Russia in June, 1942.

The Germans were frustrated in their Eastern offensive. The vastness of Russia created serious supply shortages. Following a "scorched-earth" policy, the Russians burned everything of value as they retreated. The greatest enemy the Germans faced in Russia, however, was the savage Soviet winter that forced them to halt their attack. Taking advantage of the lull, Russian soldiers trained in winter fighting staged a counterattack that successfully drove the Germans back.

Japan had sought to take advantage of British and French involvement in the war by seizing their territories in the Far East and the Pacific. The United States and British governments protested. In the latter part of 1941, the Japanese sent a delegation to Washington to negotiate these problems. The Washington peace meeting was a ruse, however. On December 7, 1941, Japan bombed the American naval base at Pearl Harbor, Hawaii. Over two thousand Americans were killed and a large number of ships and planes were sunk or destroyed. In his speech to Congress the following day, President Roosevelt said it was "a day that will live in infamy."

Congress declared war on Japan December 8, 1941. Germany immediately declared war on the United States, and Britain declared war on Japan.

From the beginning of the European conflict, Americans had been supplying the Allies with food, equipment, and ammunition. In November, 1942, American soldiers under the command of Dwight D. Eisenhower joined the Allies for the first time in North Africa where the British were already defeating the Germans under Rommel. In May, 1943, after fierce German resistance, the Allies forced the Germans to surrender in North Africa.

The Allied offensive in North Africa weakened the Germans in Russia when Hitler was forced to send reinforcements to Rommel. The Russian front had been costly to Hitler. Several months of battle had resulted in little gain against Russian resistance. Russia staged a massive counterattack in November, 1942. After two months of bitter fighting, the Germans surrendered their huge army at Stalingrad, a turning point in the war. By early 1944, the Germans had been forced off Russian soil.

In July 1943, Allied forces from North Africa landed on the island of Sicily off Italy. Although the Italian army surrendered, German divisions rushed to stop the Allied advance northward. German resistance was intense, but the Allies drove them steadily back.

The liberation of Europe from the Germans was now being planned. Prime Minister Winston Churchill and President Franklin Roosevelt conferred and appointed General Dwight Eisenhower to lead an Allied invasion of occupied northern France. It was to be a huge effort. The French coastline was heavily fortified by waiting Germans, many of whom were held in reserve for such an emergency.

Plans were made to invade France in June, 1944. Every detail was carefully planned by Eisenhower and his Allied staff. The task was immense—more than a million men and their equipment had to be transported across the English Channel.

Although the invasion of Europe on the Normandy coast of France met with strong resistance, within a month more than 1 million men, one hundred fifty thousand vehicles, and six hundred fifty thousand tons of supplies had been put ashore. From the Normandy beachhead the Allies started to drive across northern France. After pushing the Germans from the Italian peninsula, Allied forces landed in southern France as well and drove northward. On August 25, 1944, Paris fell to the liberators. By early September the Allies had driven into Belgium.

Meanwhile, the Russians closed in on the Germans from the east. They recovered Finland and the Baltic states of Estonia, Lithuania, and Latvia. Pushing through Rumania and Bulgaria, the Russians were aided on the eastern front by the British, who had driven the Germans from Greece. After seizing Yugoslavia and Albania, the Russian advance met and overcame strong German resistance in Poland.

In the face of these defeats, Hitler refused to surrender. When the Allies burst through German lines in the west, the Germans staged an immense counterattack, driving a fifty-mile bulge into the Allied line. The Battle of the Bulge was won by the Allies at a huge cost in lives to both sides.

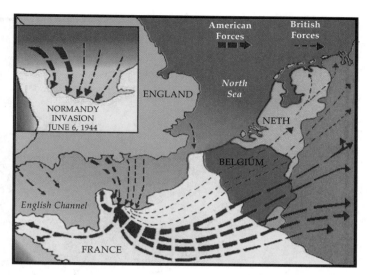

On April 25, 1945, the leaders of the United States and Russia met in the city of Torgau, seventy-five miles from Berlin, to discuss their strategy for ending the war. In view of the suffering Russians had met at the hands of the Germans, they would be permitted to enter Berlin to receive Germany's surrender. Fearing retribution for their aggression and cruelty toward the Russians, the Germans wanted to surrender to England and the United States. The Allies, however, remained firm in their earlier decision, and Berlin was surrendered to the Russians on May 2, 1945. The German army in northern Italy surrendered at the same time. Mussolini was captured and killed by Italian guerrillas; and Hitler, during the struggle for Berlin, committed suicide.

After six years of war, the German high command surrendered unconditionally to the Allies on May 8, 1945, which became known as V-E Day, the day of victory in Europe for the Allied powers.

General Eisenhower addresses troops.

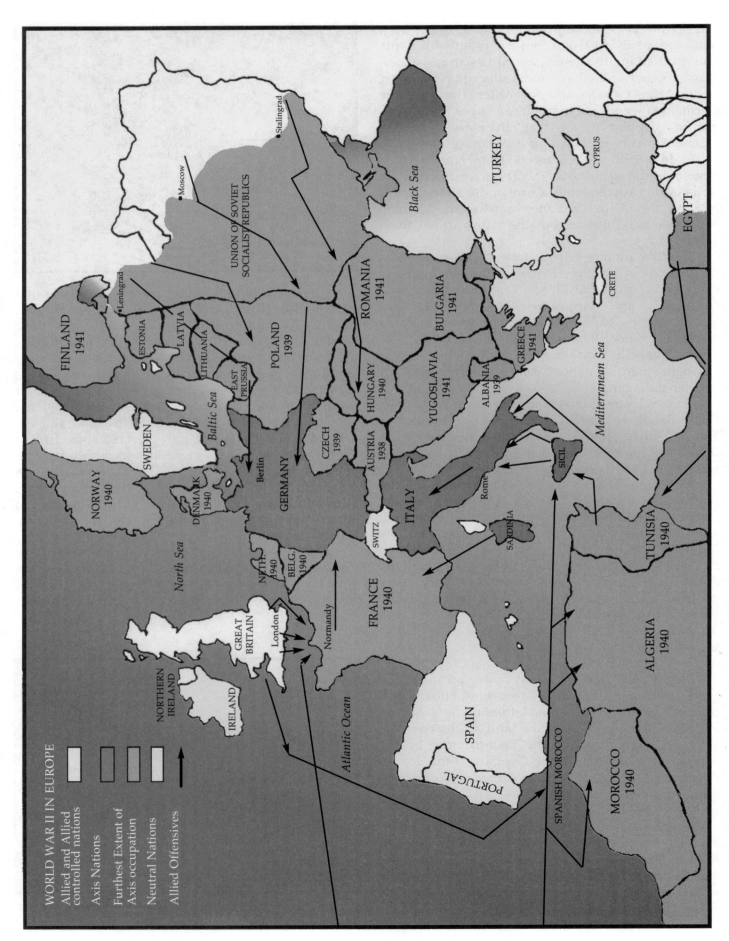

WORLD WAR II IN EUROPE

Allied and Allied controlled nations

Axis Nations

Furthest Extent of Axis occupation

Neutral Nations

Allied Offensives

FINLAND 1941

NORWAY 1940

SWEDEN

DENMARK 1940

North Sea

Baltic Sea

ESTONIA

LATVIA

LITHUANIA

EAST PRUSSIA

Leningrad

Moscow

Stalingrad

UNION OF SOVIET SOCIALIST REPUBLICS

POLAND 1939

Berlin

GERMANY

CZECH 1939

AUSTRIA 1938

HUNGARY 1940

ROMANIA 1941

BULGARIA 1941

YUGOSLAVIA 1941

ALBANIA 1939

GREECE 1941

Black Sea

TURKEY

CYPRUS

CRETE

Mediterranean Sea

EGYPT

NETH. 1940

BELG. 1940

Normandy

FRANCE 1940

SWITZ

ITALY

Rome

SARDINIA

SICIL

TUNISIA 1940

ALGERIA 1940

SPANISH MOROCCO

MOROCCO 1940

SPAIN

PORTUGAL

Atlantic Ocean

GREAT BRITAIN

London

NORTHERN IRELAND

IRELAND

Match these items.

3.1 _____ blitzkrieg   a. led Allied forces at Normandy

3.2 _____ Hitler   b. the Japanese surprise attack on American naval base

3.3 _____ Roosevelt   c. the Allied victory in Japan

3.4 _____ Churchill   d. the German war offensive

3.5 _____ Rommel   e. the German dictator, World War II

3.6 _____ Eisenhower   f. the British prime minister, World War II

3.7 _____ V-E Day   g. the United States president during World War II

3.8 _____ Pearl Harbor   h. the German commander in North Africa

     i. Allied victory in Europe

Write *true* **or** *false*.

3.9 _____ The German takeover of Denmark and Norway threatened Axis trade.

3.10 _____ The German seizure of Holland, Belgium, and Luxembourg forced the British to withdraw from the continent to England.

3.11 _____ Italy joined the Axis powers when French resistance was weakened.

3.12 _____ When Hitler gained control of the Balkan states, German relations with Russia crumbled.

3.13 _____ The French, like the Russians, put up stiff resistance to the German drive, and burned the land as they retreated.

3.14 _____ Japanese-American relations grew tense following Japanese aggression in the Pacific.

3.15 _____ Eisenhower aided the British in driving Rommel from North Africa.

3.16 _____ The Allied leaders sought to free France with the Allied invasion of Normandy on June 6.

3.17 _____ The Germans were trapped as the British and the Americans closed in from the east and the Russians closed in from the west.

3.18 _____ Due to severe losses suffered at the hands of the Germans, the Russians were given the task of seizing Berlin and receiving the German surrender.

Complete this activity.

3.19 Trace the Allied strategy for victory over the Axis powers in Europe following the entrance of the United States into the war.

_____

_____

_____

_____

_____

_____

Pacific. After the Japanese surprise attack on Pearl Harbor, the United States, although weakened, went on the offensive in the Pacific. Here, unlike Europe, the Americans stood almost alone.

With the American navy badly damaged at Pearl Harbor, Japan captured much of the western Pacific and eastern Asia. Guam, Midway, and Wake Island were taken in addition to the East Indies, the Philippines, and the Gilbert Islands. In Asia, Burma and Thailand were added to previous Japanese possessions. In a short time the Japanese held over a million square miles rich in natural resources.

When he was forced to leave the Philippines in 1942, the American General Douglas MacArthur vowed, "I shall return." Later he would spearhead the American led campaign to gain control of the Pacific from the Japanese.

Early in the Pacific campaign a decision was made to bomb Tokyo as early in the war as possible. The *Raid of Reprisal*, as it was called, would lift American morale and would show the Japanese their homeland was open to attack. Leading the raid was Lieutenant Colonel James H. Doolittle, who attacked from a navy aircraft carrier on April 13, 1942 with sixteen American planes. The raid was a success. It caused some destruction to the Japanese homeland and lifted United States morale.

When the Japanese threatened Australia in May, 1942, they received their first setback. The invasion was met by combined United States and Australian air and naval forces. The five-day battle of the Coral Sea followed, and the Japanese met defeat. When another Japanese fleet moved toward Midway Island, it was cut off and nearly destroyed.

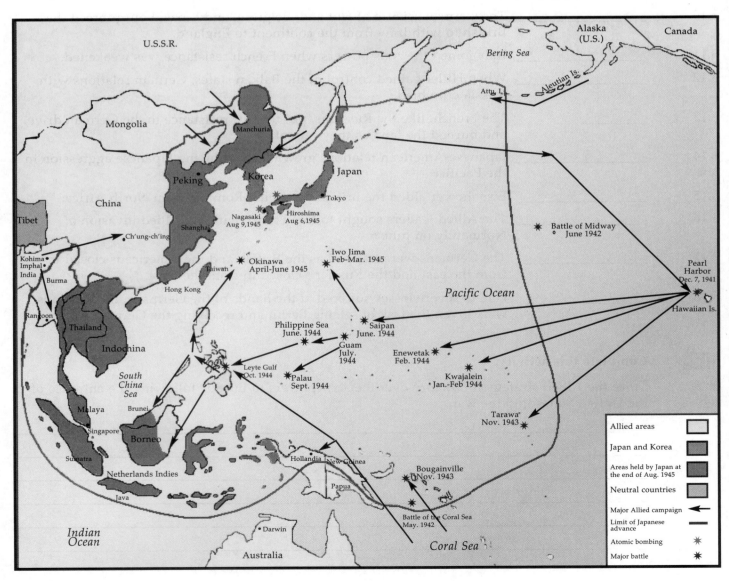

30

In early August, 1942, the United States Marines landed in the Solomon Islands and seized the airfield at Guadalcanal, a strategic location in the supply line from Hawaii and the United States to Australia. The Japanese defenders fought desperately, but the marines prevailed after great loss of life.

Combining sea, air, and land forces, the Allies took the offensive and captured the remainder of the Solomon Islands, Tarawa in the Gilbert Islands, and Attu and Kiska in the Aleutians in 1943. Following these Allied victories, the United States planned a series of island hopping conquests that would lead them almost to Japan itself.

With a rebuilt navy and reinforcements of men and supplies the forces of the United States captured the Marshall Islands, New Guinea, and the Marianas in 1944. United States victories in the battles of the Philippine Sea and Leyte Gulf paved the way for a landing in the Philippines in 1945. True to his departing words, General MacArthur had returned.

With the success of the Allied island-hopping campaign, the main islands of Japan were now within range of United States bombers. Japan's cities were methodically bombed. In an attempt to get closer, the Marines landed on Iwo Jima in 1945 and took the island after a month of terrible bloodshed. The Allies attacked Okinawa in June and wrested it from the Japanese. So close were they to the Japanese homeland now that thousands of desperate Japanese **kamikaze** pilots in planes rigged with explosives crashed themselves into U.S. ships.

An invasion of Japan would be costly; a million United States casualties would result. Thus, President Truman decided to use the atomic bomb in war for the first time. Atomic bombs were dropped on Hiroshima August 6 and on Nagasaki August 9. Tens of thousands of people were killed.

The dropping of the atomic bombs continues to be controversial, but it brought a Japanese surrender on September 2, 1945.

Complete these statements.

3.20   While the United States recovered from the Japanese attack at Pearl Harbor, Japan quickly extended its control throughout the _____.

3.21   The general chosen to lead American forces in the war against Japan in the Pacific was

_____.

3.22   The war in the Pacific was largely naval, and the island fighting was done by United States

_____.

3.23   Americans received a psychological lift with the raid on Tokyo by_____.

3.24   The United States' recovery of the Philippines was accomplished through the battles of the

a. _____ and the b. _____.

3.25   Japanese pilots who crashed their planes into American ships in a desperate defense of their homeland were called _____.

3.26   Atomic bombs were dropped at a. _____ and

b. _____.

Write the correct letter on each line.

3.27 The United States received no aid in the Pacific from their European ally _____ .
  a. China   c. Britain
  b. Australia   d. France

3.28 A strategic United States victory in the Pacific in World War II was the battle of _____ .
  a. Chateau-Thierry   c. Moscow
  b. Berlin   d. Leyte Gulf

3.29 Bombing of Japan by the United States took place from _____ .
  a. Midway   c. Iwo Jima
  b. Guam   d. Solomon Islands

Complete these activities.

3.30 With a classmate, weigh the advantages and disadvantages of the atomic bombing of Japan, giving arguments for both sides of the issue.

  a. advantages: _____

  _____

  _____

  _____

  _____

  b. disadvantages: _____

  _____

  _____

  _____

3.31 Doolittle's *Raid of Reprisal* was an act of retaliation and vengeance for the Japanese bombing of Pearl Harbor. This action is understandable in times of war, but what does the Bible have to say about vengeance in our daily lives?

  _____

  _____

  _____

  _____

  _____

PEACE EFFORTS

Throughout World War II, the leaders met not only to discuss Allied war strategy but also to plan for the postwar period.

In August, 1941, President Roosevelt and Prime Minister Churchill met at sea off the coast of Newfoundland. The result of the conference was the Atlantic Charter, a document setting out democracy's goals in the war. Similar to Wilson's Fourteen Points, the charter stated that neither nation sought any gain from the war and that both nations would strive to restore self-government to nations that had fallen under totalitarian control. The charter held out hope to conquered nations and to citizens of the Axis powers should their dictatorships be overthrown.

Roosevelt and Churchill met often during the war. These meetings sometimes included other world leaders. The Yalta Conference, which began February 4, 1945, included Roosevelt, Churchill, and Stalin of the Soviet Union. The men discussed war strategy in the Pacific and settlements in Europe and the Pacific. Russia was to be given almost half of prewar Poland and was promised the Kuril Islands and control of Manchuria. Separate zones for Allied occupation of Germany after the war were also decided at the meeting.

The three Allied leaders, Truman, Stalin, and Churchill, met in July and August, 1945, at Potsdam, a suburb of Berlin. In an effort to prevent Germany from starting another war, the Allied leaders divided it into occupation zones under the United States (⅙), British (⅙), French (⅙), and Russian (½) control. Germany would be governed temporarily by the occupying nations. A permanent government would be established later.

Russia wanted to cripple German industry following the war to prevent it from ever becoming powerful again. The other Allies considered industry vital to German reconstruction so long as it was not put to military use.

The Allied nations agreed that Nazi war criminals should be punished. War crimes trials were held in Nuremberg, Germany from October, 1945, until October, 1946. Prosecutors from the United States, Britain, and Russia tried former Nazis for mass murder and crimes against humanity. Similar trials took place later against some Japanese in the Pacific.

Settlements. In July, 1946, representatives of twenty-one of the United Nations met in Paris to write peace treaties with Italy, Hungary, Bulgaria, Rumania, and Finland. They were signed by the United States, Britain, Russia, and France in Paris on February 10, 1947. The treaties determined the division of the defeated powers, set the boundaries of their territory, established reparation payments, and placed limits on their military capability. Although German occupation had already been determined at the Potsdam Conference, treaties with Germany and Austria still had to be decided. In 1947 representatives of the four major powers—the United States, Russia, Britain, and France—met in Moscow to discuss the German and Austrian treaties.

The United States and Russia clashed in Moscow when Russia demanded large reparations from Germany for the damage it caused in the war. The United States reasoned that harsh reparations would cripple the German economy. The Moscow meeting ended in a stalemate.

In 1948 Russia attempted to drive the other occupying countries out of Germany by blockading West Berlin. In a move to unify their strength in Berlin, the democracies combined their zones in 1949 and formed a new nation, the Federal Republic of Germany. Russia then established its zone, East Germany, into the German Democratic Republic. After efforts by the United States to establish a joint American-Russian peace treaty with Germany failed, the United States passed a peace agreement with West Germany alone.

Austria, too, had been divided into occupation zones after the war. In Austria, as in Germany, repeated efforts to reach a peace agreement ended in deadlocks over reparations and boundary lines. The four occupation powers finally signed an Austrian peace settlement in May, 1955, making Austria an independent, democratic nation once again.

Efforts to establish a peace treaty with Japan were also thwarted by disagreements between the United States and Russia. Finally, in 1951 the United States worked out a treaty acceptable to Japan and forty-eight other nations. Although Russia refused to sign, the treaty went into effect. By its terms, Japan was required to give up all territories it had seized since 1894. Manchuria, Formosa, and the Pescadores Islands were returned to China; and Korea was allowed to become a free and independent nation. Japan would be occupied by Allied troops until the Allied nations agreed to allow its independence.

To stimulate the Japanese economy, reparations were made to other nations only in the form of Japanese manufactured goods made from raw materials supplied by the injured nations. No limitations were set on the Japanese military, but Japan had to abide by nonaggression conditions of the United Nations Charter.

The signing of the peace settlement with Japan at last brought World War II to an end.

**The leaders of the Allied nations:
Stalin, Roosevelt, and Churchill.**

Identify the following names.

3.32   Roosevelt   _____

3.33   Churchill   _____

3.34   Stalin   _____

3.35   Atlantic Charter   _____

3.36   United Nations   _____

3.37   Federal Republic of Germany   _____

3.38   German Democratic Republic   _____

Write the letter of the correct answer on each line.

3.39   Allied meetings to determine war and postwar policies and strategies were held in every place
       but _____ .
       a. Yalta
       b. Potsdam
       c. Tokyo
       d. Newfoundland
       e. Paris

3.40   Allied nations occupying Germany and Austria included every nation except _____ .
       a. Russia
       b. Belgium
       c. France
       d. United States
       e. Great Britain

3.41   Allied treaties with the defeated European nations contained every provision *except* to
       _____ .
       a. set reparations
       b. limit their military
       c. set boundaries
       d. cripple their industry
       e. divide their land and colonies

3.42   In establishing peace treaties, the United States and Russia clashed over a. _____ and
       b. _____ .
       a. reparations
       b. industrial limitations
       c. the punishment of war criminals

3.43   In its treaty, Japan was required to do everything *except* _____ .
       a. give up territories it seized since 1894
       b. severely limit its military
       c. allow Korea to become free
       d. return territory to China
       e. pay reparations in the form of manufactured goods

3.44   According to the Bible, how successful would the world's attempts be at lasting peace?

_____

_____

_____

_____

_____

Unification. While World War II was still raging, in 1943 Allied leaders had expressed their desire to establish an international organization to ensure future world peace. In the Moscow meeting of 1943, the representatives of Britain, Russia, China, and the United States signed an agreement to plan such an organization.

The nations convened again in August, 1944, in Washington D.C., where they designed the framework upon which the United Nations would be built.

The United Nations Charter was endorsed by representatives from fifty nations in San Francisco on April 25, 1945. Its originator, President Roosevelt, died thirteen days before the San Francisco conference made his dream for a world organization a reality. The charter was then submitted to the governments for Ratification. The charter states:

WE, THE PEOPLES OF THE UNITED NATIONS, Determined

—to save succeeding generations from the scourge of war, which twice in our lifetime has brought untold sorrow to mankind, and

—to reaffirm faith in fundamental human rights, in the dignity and worth of the human person, in the equal rights of men and women and of nations large and small, and

—to establish conditions under which justice and respect for the obligations arising from treaties and other sources of international law can be maintained, and

—to promote social progress and better standards of life in larger freedom,
And For These Ends

—to practice tolerance and live together in peace with one another as good neighbors, and

—to unite our strength to maintain international peace and security, and

—to ensure, by the acceptance of principles and the institution of methods, that armed force shall not be used, save in the common interest, and

—to employ international machinery for the promotion of the economic and social advancement of all peoples,

Have Resolved To Combine Our Efforts To Accomplish These Aims.

Aware of Woodrow Wilson's failure to gain Senate acceptance of the League of Nations, Roosevelt chose respected national leaders to represent the United States in the San Francisco talks. His insight paid off—the United Nations Charter was approved by the United States Senate on July 28, 1945. Within four months, fifty-one nations had signed; and the charter became effective on October 24, 1945.

The main body of the United Nations is the General Assembly, composed of delegates from all of the member nations. Normally the assembly convenes once a year unless a special meeting is required. The meetings are conducted as a forum: Any problem can be introduced, and opinions concerning the issue can be freely voiced. The assembly acts only as a sounding board, however, where views are voiced and policies are recommended.

The Security Council is the action arm of the United Nations. Composed of eleven members, five are permanent—the United States, Great Britain, Russia, France, and Communist China—and the remaining six are elected at two-year intervals. The council has the authority to maintain peace, to settle disputes, and to stop aggression by military means if necessary. Seven members must agree before any action is taken, including all five permanent members.

The Secretariat of the United Nations is composed of clerical and administrative workers and advisers to the organization. Headed by the Secretary-General, the Secretariat contains permanent employees of the United Nations. The Secretary-General, who serves for five years, is elected by the General Assembly and reports to the annual convention any work of the United Nations organization.

Opening day of the General Assembly, 50th anniversary-1995

Thus, he attends all meetings of any branch of the United Nations and may make recommendations even to the Security Council. The International Court of Justice is another branch of the United Nations. Composed of fifteen judges appointed by the Security Council and the General Assembly, the court settles disputes brought willingly before it by national governments. It has no authority, however, to force the nations involved to accept the court's decision; it can only make a ruling.

Although the United Nations has been criticized, it has survived and proves Franklin D. Roosevelt's motto, "It's better to jaw than to war."The United Nations has resolved a number of world crises, but deadlocks have resulted through disagreements between its two most powerful members, the United States and the former Soviet Union. Only as strong as its members allow it to be, the United Nations was repeatedly thwarted in its ability to act by the votes of the USSR.

The United Nations has been troubled by the world-wide plague of all organizations—politics. Many nations vote to promote their own agendas rather than to solve problems. Hostility between nations often interferes in fair judgement on issues. The use of United Nations organizations to promote abortion and other controversial programs has caused conflict. The U.N. has gotten deeply in debt as countries have refused or been unable to pay their dues—this, at a time when small wars in the world have taxed U.N. resources. The U.N. has sent expensive "peacekeeping troops" to many nations to monitor truces and to try to halt wars.

Nevertheless, the U.N. has had some notable successes. South Korea was successfully defended against communist aggression in the 1950s under the U.N. banner. The U.N. has been the primary negotiator in several peace agreements, including the Six-Day War in Israel (1967). The U.N. officially led the freeing of Kuwait during the Persian Gulf War (1990-91). Moreover, the U.N. has many groups fighting world hunger, oppression, and poverty. So, for all of its problems, the United Nations has been a useful voice in the modern world community.

EUROPE 1950

■ Annexed areas after World War II
■ NATO Nations
□ Neutral Nations
■ Communist Nations
╂╂╂╂╂ Iron Curtain

FINLAND
NORWAY
ESTONIA
GREAT BRITAIN
SWEDEN
LITHUANIA
North Sea
Baltic Sea
IRELAND
Atlantic Ocean
GERMAN DEM REP
Berlin
POLAND
NETH
FEDERAL GERMAN REPUBLIC
SOVIET ZONE
BELGIUM
CZECHOSLOVAKIA
UKRAINE
FRANCE
SWITZ.
AUSTRIA
HUNGARY
ROMANIA
PORTUGAL
Black Sea
YUGOSLAVIA
BULGARIA
SPAIN
CORSICA
ITALY
ALBANIA
TURKEY
SARDINIA
Mediterranean Sea
SPANISH MOROCCO
SICILY
MOROCCO
ALGERIA
TUNISIA

Complete the following activity.

3.45   Fill in the information on the United Nations on the lines that follow.

		Members		Duties
A. General Assembly	1.	_____	2.	_____
		_____		_____
B. Security Council	1.	_____	2.	_____
		_____		_____
C. Secretariat	1.	_____	2.	_____
		_____		_____
D. Secretary-General	1.	_____	2.	_____
		_____		_____
E. International Court of Justice	1.	_____	2.	_____
		_____		_____

Write *true* **or** *false.*

3.46 _____ The United Nations was largely designed by Theodore Roosevelt.

3.47 _____ Wilson's United Nations failed to receive Senate support.

3.48 _____ United Nations policy is to settle problems peacefully rather than through war.

3.49 _____ Many deadlocks in the United Nations have resulted from differences between the United States and China.

3.50 _____ The USSR repeatedly used its vote in the UN to thwart that agency's ability to act.

3.51 _____ The United Nations charter was signed in New York City in 1945.

3.52 _____ The UN forces were successful in freeing Kuwait during the Persian Gulf War.

Complete this activity.

3.53 With a classmate, list as many strengths and weaknesses of the United Nations as you can. Give solutions to the weaknesses.

strengths: _____

_____

_____

_____

_____

_____

weaknesses	solutions
_____	_____
_____	_____
_____	_____
_____	_____
_____	_____

Select a project.

3.54 Choose one of the following research projects for this LIFEPAC's extended writing assignment.

a. Research the major functions of the United Nations since its beginning and make a compilation of five of its greatest successes and five of its defeats. Describe each in detail.

b. Research a major offensive of World War I or II and report on it in detail, accompanying your report with battle charts.

c. Write a biography on one of the following leaders: Hitler, Mussolini, Churchill, Eisenhower, MacArthur, Stalin, Roosevelt, or Wilson.

SelfTest

Before you take this last Self Test, you may want to do one or more of these self checks.

1. _____ Read the objectives. See if you can do them.

2. _____ Restudy the material related to any objectives that you cannot do.

3. _____ Use the SQ3R study procedure to review the material:

    a. **S**can the sections.

    b. **Q**uestion yourself.

    c. **R**ead to answer your questions.

    d. **R**ecite the answers to yourself.

    e. **R**eview areas you did not understand.

4. _____ Review all vocabulary, activities, and Self Tests, writing a correct answer for every wrong answer.

SELF TEST 3

Match these items (each answer, 2 points).

3.01	_____ Bismarck	a.	United States president, World War I
3.02	_____ Wilhelm	b.	British prime minister, World War II
3.03	_____ Ferdinand	c.	led the Allied invasion of Normandy, World War II
3.04	_____ Wilson	d.	led United States troops in Pacific, World War II
3.05	_____ Mussolini	e.	German dictator, World War II
3.06	_____ Hitler	f.	Russian dictator, World War I
3.07	_____ Roosevelt	g.	the assassinated Austrian archduke
3.08	_____ Churchill	h.	German chancellor prior to World War I
3.09	_____ Stalin	i.	United States president, World War II
3.010	_____ Eisenhower	j.	Japanese suicide pilots
3.011	_____ MacArthur	k.	German emperor, World War I
3.012	_____ *kamikaze*	l.	Italian fascist dictator, World War II
3.013	_____ Rommel	m.	German commander in North Africa, World War II
		n.	Russian premier, World War II

Complete these statements (each answer, 3 points).

3.014 Loyalty of a people to their country is called _____ .

3.015 Extending the rule or authority of one country over another country or colonies is called
_____ .

3.016 The alliance formed to balance the power of Europe upset by the formation of the Triple Alliance was the _____ .

3.017 Germany was a member of the Central powers in World War I, and the _____ powers in World War II.

3.018 Confirmation or approval by a government is called _____ .

3.019 The Bolsheviks came into power in the Soviet Union as a result of the _____ .

3.020 The proposed terms for a just peace following World War I were Wilson's
_____ .

3.021 The organization established to ensure world peace following World War I was
_____ .

3.022 The segment of the Peace of Paris relating to the German settlement was the
_____ .

3.023 A government which controls its people and their activities is called a _____ government.

3.024 The organization established for peaceful settlements of world problems after World War II was the _____ .

3.025 As a result of the peace treaty with the United States, Japan had to return _____ ,
_____ , and the _____ to China.

3.026 The United Nations Charter was signed in the city of _____ in
_____ .

3.027 The agreement by Roosevelt and Churchill declaring their countries had no interest in personal gains in the war was the _____ .

Write *true* **or** *false* (each answer, 1 point).

3.028 _____ Bismarck established peaceful relations with England and Russia to isolate France.

3.029 _____ The assassination of the Archduke Ferdinand set off a chain reaction of nations declaring war in World War I.

3.030 _____ The advocates of a lenient peace prevailed in the Peace of Paris.

3.031 _____ Because other nations were dependent on American loans, America's Great Depression was felt worldwide.

3.032 _____ Aggressive nations prior to World War II were Japan, Germany, and France.

3.033 _____ Hitler and Mussolini increased their nations' military strength to lift them from the depression.

3.034 _____ When Hitler invaded Poland, Britain and France declared war on Germany.

3.035 _____ The decision to drop atomic bombs on Japan was made partly because of the large number of casualties expected in a land invasion.

3.036 _____ In establishing World War II peace treaties, the United States and Russia clashed over reparations and industrial limitations.

3.037 _____ The League of Nations received full Senate support in the United States.

3.038 _____ U.N. troops defended South Korea against Communist aggression in the 1950s.

3.039 _____ The Security Council can recommend United Nations action, but only the General Assembly has the authority to enforce it.

Write the letter for the correct choice on each line (each answer, 2 points).

3.040 The incident which set off World War I was _____ .
   a. military armament
   b. nationalism
   c. assassination of Archduke Ferdinand
   d. imperialism

3.041 The final German defeat in World War I was due to the _____ .
   a. Allied drive of 1918
   b. Normandy invasion
   c. stand at Chateau-Thierry
   d. Russian Revolution

3.042 The post-World War I mood in Germany was _____ .
   a. prosperous
   b. pleasure-seeking
   c. bitter over economic depression
   d. lifted by the Treaty of Versailles

3.043 World War II began over the _____ .
   a. rise of totalitarianism
   b. invasion of Poland
   c. economic depression
   d. fall of Austria

3.044   A strategic offensive in the Allied drive against the Axis powers in Europe in World War II was
        the _____ .
        a.   attack on Pearl Harbor
        b.   stand at Chateau-Thierry
        c.   Normandy invasion
        d.   takeover of England

3.045   American strategy in the Pacific included _____ .
        a.   land invasion of Japan
        b.   island-hopping
        c.   march on Berlin
        d.   surrender of China

Answer these questions (each answer, 5 points).

3.046   What was the significance of these actions?

        a.   Ferdinand's assassination _____

             _____

        b.   Bombing of *Lusitania* _____

             _____

        c.   Pearl Harbor attack _____

             _____

        d.   UN Charter _____

             _____

        e.   Military build-ups _____

             _____

3.047   Why was the United Nations more successful than the League of Nations?

        _____

        _____

        _____

        _____

        98
        _____
        122

Score _____

Teacher check _____
               Initial   Date

Before taking the LIFEPAC Test, you may want to do one or more of these self checks.

    1.   _____   Read the objectives. See if you can do them.
    2.   _____   Restudy the material related to any objectives that you cannot do.
    3.   _____   Use the SQ3R study procedure to review the material.
    4.   _____   Review activities, Self Tests, and LIFEPAC vocabulary words.
    5.   _____   Restudy areas of weakness indicated by the last Self Test.

GLOSSARY

armament—War equipment and supplies.

blitzkrieg—A swift, sudden attack by tanks, aircraft and so forth.

conscription—A compulsory enrollment of men for military service; draft.

demilitarize—To remove military equipment and troops from a place and declare it neutral.

fascism—A one-party system of government in which each class has its distinct place but the individual is subject to the state and control is maintained by military force, secret police, and governmental regimentation of industry and finance.

imperialism—The development of forcing trade and exploration of raw materials of backward countries through political or military means.

kamikaze—In World War II, the suicidal Japanese tactic of ramming ships with a piloted airplane carrying explosives.

nationalism—Devotion to one's nation and to its political, social, and cultural interests and traditions.

ratification—The act of giving approval or confirmation.

recession—An economic setback in commercial and industrial activity.

reparations—Indemnities paid by defeated countries for acts of war.

reprisal—The application of force by one nation against another in retaliation for acts committed.

totalitarianism—A one-party government maintained by political suppression usually combined with cultural and economic controls.